Printed in China.

Produced by Via Press, LLC, Phoenix, Arizona

Cover and interior design by Christy A. Masel,
Phoenix, Arizona

Compiled by Jennifer S. Kaye
Touch With Intention
Scottsdale, Arizona

ISBN: 1-930408-33-1

Lawrence Teacher Publishing Group, LLC
4701 Bath Street
Philadelphia, PA 19137

LITTLE BOOK OF
RELAXATION

Compiled by Jennifer Kaye

table of contents

By Jennifer Kaye

Now more than ever we race through life, every moment filled with activity. We work and we work out. We take care of our homes. We hangout with our friends. We surf the 'Net, talk on the phone, travel, and shop. Too often, however, we do not take the time to just RELAX.

Ironically, relaxing is the most important activity that we can do all day! Unless we take time for ourselves and fill the cup of our being, we are less effective, tire more easily, and create more stress in our daily lives.

Although we often find relaxation during vacation, it is by creating mini-vacations and taking just a few minutes for ourselves each day that we acquire the greatest benefit. Whether it is taking the time to breathe, to laugh, or to rest, by just practicing a few simple activities every day, we can refresh and rejuvenate our bodies, our minds, and our spirits.

This *Little Book of Relaxation* is designed to offer simple, practical, daily actions for relaxation. It is through practice that we become better at anything we do. May this book offer you simple reminders to take a moment for yourself each day and just practice the fine art of relaxation.

The sound of a waterfall in the distance,

mimicking the gentle laughter of lovers.

The scent of flowers in your hair, and the beauty

JUST RELAX

re-lax

1. To make loose
2. To relieve from tension or strain
3. To take one's ease; rest
4. Refreshment of body or mind

• *The American Heritage Dictionary* •

RELAX AT THE BEGINNING OF THE DAY

Morning Exercise

1. Light a candle instead of turning on the light.
2. Allow your eyes to adjust.
3. S-T-R-E-E-E-T-C-H.
4. Take five deep breaths.
5. Now get out of bed.

RELAX AT THE END OF THE DAY

Nighttime Ritual

1. This day is now done.
2. Think about what challenged you or was left undone.
3. Take three to five deep breaths and release it.

Put duties aside at least an hour before bed and perform soothing, quiet activities that will help you relax.

• *Dianne Hales* •

Finish each day and be done with it. You have done what you could. Some blunders and absurdities no doubt crept in. Forget them as soon as you can. Tomorrow is a new day. Begin it well and serenely and with too high a spirit to be encumbered with your old nonsense.

• Ralph Waldo Emerson •

True silence is
rest of the mind;
it is to the spirit what
sleep is to the body;
nourishment and
refreshment.

• William Penn •

This art of resting the mind and the power of dismissing from it all care and worry, is probably one of the secrets of energy in our great men.

• Captain J.A. Hadfield •

We are cups,
constantly and
quietly being filled.
The trick is knowing
how to tip ourselves
over and let the
beautiful stuff out.

• *Ray Bradbury* •

JUST BREATHE

Breathing helps our
bodies to relax,
giving us an
opportunity to
rejuvenate.

**Whatever you are
doing right now:**

- STOP

- Inhale

- EXHALE

- Uncrease your
  eyebrows

- Lift the corners of your mouth

- Inhale

- Exhale

- PERFECT

Breathing is a
two-part process.
The **inhale** is
everything we
receive.
The **exhale** is
everything we
release.

What do you want to
receive right now?
What do you want to
release right now?

A Relaxation Breath

1. Inhale to a count of 7
2. Hold the breath for a count of 7
3. Exhale for a count of 7

While you exhale, think of all the things that are challenging you today and release them.

I am open to
receive with every
breath I breathe.

• Michael Sun •

The next time you have to stand in a line, rather than focusing on the inconvenience, take this time to relax. Take a deep breath, lower your shoulders, take another deep breath, and relax.

Fear less, hope more;
eat less, chew more;
whine less,
breathe more;
talk less, say more;
hate less, love more;
and all good things
are yours.

• *Swedish Proverb* •

Give me
some breath,
some little pause.

• *Shakespeare* •

Simple Ways to Breathe Deeply Throughout the Day

At the office:

1. As you turn on the computer, take three deep breaths.
2. When the phone rings take a deep breath before answering.
3. Hang the phone up, take another deep breath, and re-focus on your task at hand.

No matter how much pressure you feel at work, if you could find ways to relax for at least five minutes every hour, you'd be more productive.

• *Dr. Joyce Brothers* •

Every now and then go away, have a little relaxation, for when you come back to your work your judgement will be surer. Go some distance away because then the work appears smaller and more of it can be taken in at a glance and a lack of harmony and proportion is more readily seen.

• *Leonardo Da Vinci* •

The sword outwears
its sheath, and the
soul wears out the
breast. And the heart
must pause to
breathe, and love
itself have rest.

• *Lord Byron* •

In the car:

1. When you come to a red light, take two cleansing breaths.
2. Turn the radio off. In the silence, take two or three deep breaths.

At home:

1. Upon arriving home, instead of turning on the television or the computer right away, just be silent. Luxuriate in the space of your home, and breathe.

2. Just before dinner, as everyone is sitting down, take a moment of silence and 2 or 3 deep breaths. Be

grateful for the day,
for your family, for your
accomplishments.

3. Just as you sit down
to pay the bills, take a
deep breath in. EXHALE.
As you finish paying
each one, repeat the
breath. Do this with
each payment! Allow
your shoulders to drop
away from your ears.
This will help you to
relax around money.

JUST MEDITATE

med-i-tate

To train, calm or
empty the mind.
To think or reflect,
especially in a calm
and deliberate
manner.

*• The American
Heritage Dictionary •*

Mindful Meditation

1. Find a quiet place.
2. Close your eyes.
3. Notice how you feel in your body.
4. Wherever you are tense, send your breath to that area.

Meditation gives
us a moment to
pause and reflect.
It is in this momentary
suspension of time
that we can change
how stress affects us.

A Stress-Relieving Meditation

1. Find a quiet space.
2. Close your eyes and fill your mind with everything that is creating stress for you at this moment.
3. Give yourself permission to release the stress from your body,
4. Breathe in, and allow calming pictures to fill your mind.

To meditate is to
listen with a
receptive heart.

• *Jack Kornfield* •

Learn to get in touch
with silence within
yourself, and know
that everything in this
life has purpose.
There are no mistakes,
no coincidences,
all events are
blessings given to
us to learn from.

Elisabeth Kubler Ross

JUST YOGA

Our limitations and
success will be
based, most often,
on your own
expectations
for ourselves.
What the mind
dwells upon, the
body acts upon.

• Denis Waitley •

In yoga, there is a pose that is dedicated to total relaxation. It is called 'Savasana,' or Corpse Pose.

1. Find a quiet place where you can lie down on your back.
2. Place your arms beside your body with the palms turned upward.
3. Relax your feet, keeping the heels close with the toes turned slightly out.
4. Breathe (stay here for 4-6 minutes).

Relax the Body Exercise

1. Lie down on your back in a comfortable position with your palms turned upward.
2. As you inhale, tense your ankles, feet, and toes.
3. Hold the breath while you tighten the muscles.
4. Exhale and relax.

Move up the body repeating this exercise: calves, kneecaps, thighs, hamstrings, buttocks, hips, abdomen, chest, shoulders, arms and elbows, wrists, hands and fingers, all the muscles of the face, the forehead, mouth and throat.

Exhale and relax after each body part. Let any strain just melt into the floor and leave your body.

Child's Pose

1. Kneel on the floor.
2. Touch your big toes together and sit on your heels, then separate your knees about as wide as your hips.
3. If you are uncomfortable sitting on your heels, place a folded towel or blanket between your thighs and calves.

4. Exhale and lay your torso down between your thighs.

5. Lay your hands on the floor alongside your torso, palms up, and release the fronts of your shoulders toward the floor.

Child's Pose is a resting pose. Stay anywhere from 30 seconds to a few minutes.

JUST MASSAGE

A "Touch-Up" Facial Massage

1. Press your middle finger pads into the ridge of the inside of your eye sockets, right where they meet the bridge of the nose.
2. Press upward with gentle pressure.

3. Continue to apply slight pressure and follow the brow line out to the temples.
4. Repeat beginning at the inside of the eye and tracing the ridge of the bone just below each eye socket.

For tension and tight muscles, make your own massage oil!

To Relax
- 4-6 oz. of almond oil or grapeseed oil
- Add 2 tsp. vitamin E oil
- 6 drops lavender essential oil
- Apply to the area with long, flowing strokes

To Uplift

- 4-6 oz. almond or grapeseed oil
- Add 6 drops of peppermint, lemon or bergamot essential oils
- Apply to the back of the neck, or put a drop or two on each temple

For Sore Muscles

- 4-6 oz. almond or grapeseed oil
- Add 6 drops of rosemary, lavender or grapefruit essential oils
- Apply to the upper back and shoulders

Create a Peaceful Environment

- Add 3 drops of rose, geranium, or ylang ylang essential oils to a bowl of distilled water and allow the fragrance to lightly fill the room

To Relieve Pressure Headaches

1. Place your index and middle finger pads gently on your temples.
2. Press gently upward.
3. Massage lightly in small circles.

For Headaches

- Take 2 drops of lavender or 1 drop of lavender and 1 drop of peppermint.
- Apply in light brushing strokes to the forehead and temples.
- Apply with light pressure to the temples, using your index and middle fingers. Move the

fingers together in a small, circular motion.

—— OR ——

- Apply to the base of the skull, where the neck meets the head.
- Apply a slight pressure to the tender spots along the base and let the aroma penetrate the area.

Hand Massage

1. Using the thumb and index finger of your left hand, gently squeeze the padding between the thumb and index finger of your right hand
2. Repeat, massaging between the tendons of the other fingers.
3. Press and massage the tips of the thumb and each finger, pressing on the top with the thumb and on the bottom with the index finger.

4. Gently work your way up each joint of the fingers, massaging in small circular motions around each joint.

5. Be sure to massage along the sides of the thumb and fingers as well.

6. Then gently pull each finger forward in a stretching motion, and allow the thumb and supporting fingers to slide gently down to the tip of the finger, along the nail, and release.

JUST REST

What is without
periods of rest
will not endure.

• Ovid •

The Perfect Nap

1. Close the door and turn off the phone.
2. Set a time that works best for you. 5-10 minutes is fine!

3. Curl up with a few
fluffy pillows and
cozy blankets.
4. Close your eyes
and allow yourself
to rejuvenate and
recharge.

Let us be silent that
we may hear the
whispers of the gods.

• *Ralph Waldo Emerson* •

Light be the earth
upon you,
lightly rest.

• *Euripides* •

Take a rest;
a field that has
rested gives a
bountiful crop.

• *Ovid* •

He that can
take rest is greater
than he that can
take cities.

• *Benjamin Franklin* •

JUST FEET

Let stress drain away from your body with a soothing peppermint foot bath.

1. Fill a basin with enough hot water to cover your ankles.
2. Add 6-10 drops of peppermint oil.
3. Sit and soak for 10-15 minutes.
4. Wrap feet in a thick warm towel when done and gently pat dry.

A Sole Evening

1. Begin with a peppermint foot bath.
2. Pat feet dry with a warm towel.
3. Massage feet with a sea salt scrub.
4. Rinse feet thoroughly with warm water.
5. Pat dry.
6. Follow scrub with a moisturizing massage cream.

JUST EYES

The real voyage
of discovery consists
not in seeking new
landscapes but in
having new eyes.

• Marcel Proust •

We live in a wonderful world that is full of beauty, charm, and adventure. There is no end to the adventures that we can have if only we seek them with our eyes open.

• *Jawaharlal Nehru* •

When the eyes
say one thing
and the tongue
another, the
practiced person
relies on the
language of the first.

• *Ralph Waldo Emerson* •

To Relax Your Eyes

1. Run a washcloth under warm water and ring dry.
2. Lay down and cover your eyes.
3. Slowly breathe in through your nose for a count of 3.
4. Exhale through your mouth to a count of 3.
5. Let yourself drift for three to five minutes.

To any artist,
worthy of the name,
all in nature is
beautiful, because
his eyes, fearlessly
accepting all exterior
truth, read there,
as in an open book,
all the inner truth.

• *Auguste Rodin* •

No one can lie,
no one can hide
anything, when he
looks directly into
someone's eyes.

• *Paulo Coehlo* •

JUST LAUGH

Have you ever noticed that when one person laughs, everyone laughs? Relaxation is the same way!

Laughter is one
of our greatest
relaxation tools.
Studies show that
laughing lowers
blood pressure,
reduces stress
hormones, and
triggers the release
of endorphins.

People who laugh
actually live longer
than those who
don't laugh.
Few persons realize
that health actually
varies according
to the amount
of laughter.

• Dr. James Walsh •

If a man insisted
always on being
serious, and never
allowed himself a bit
of fun and relaxation,
he would go mad or
become unstable
without knowing it.

• *Herodotus* •

Life can be wildly
tragic at times, and
I've had my share.
But whatever
happens to you,
you have to
keep a slightly
comic attitude.
In the final analysis,
you have got to not
forget to laugh.

• *Katherine Hepburn* •

I think that wherever
your journey takes
you, there are new
gods waiting there,
with divine patience
– and laughter.

• *Susan M. Watkins* •

Laughter is the
closest thing to the
grace of God.

• *Karl Barth* •

Hearty laughter
is a good way
to jog internally
without having
to go outdoors.

• *Norman Cousins* •

Laughter is a highly
addictive positive
contagious;
if somebody starts,
it's very difficult
to stop.

• *Robert Holden* •

JUST TAKE TIME
FOR YOU

Today is not a race.

By taking time
for YOU,
you WILL accomplish
your goals.

Do just one thing for YOU today:

- Buy yourself flowers
- Leave work 10 minutes early
- Take a nap
- Take a bath
- Get a foot rub
- Have dessert
- Turn the phone OFF

Tell Everyone the Next Ten Minutes are YOUR Time:

- Make your own "Do Not Disturb" sign.
- Read fiction. Don't think, just read.
- Lose yourself in a good book.
- Sit in front of the fireplace.
- Play a board game.
- Let the kids order out for dinner.

At Supper Time

1. Dim the lights and light some candles.
2. Turn on some easy, relaxing music in the background.
3. Savor each bite and taste the full flavor of your meal.
4. Have family members take turns doing the dishes so for one night, you can just relax!

Think in the morning.
Act in the noon.
Eat in the evening.
Sleep in the night.

• William Blake •

Instead of coming right home and turning on the television or computer, set aside time each day to:

- Listen to some relaxing music while cooking dinner
- Enjoy the silence
- Spend extra time talking with family members

Television has proved
that people will look
at anything rather
than each other.

• *Ann Landers* •

Music for Relaxation

- **Prayer -**
  A Windham Hill Collection
- **Effortless Relaxation -**
  Steven Halpern
- **Domenico Scarlatti -**
  Keyboard Sonatas –
  Mikhail Pletnev
- **The Most Relaxing Classical Album in the World…Ever! -**
  Johann Sebastian Bach
- **Mozart: The Piano Sonatas -**
  Andras Schiff
- **Season of Souls -**
  Tulku

- **Towards the Wind -**
  Stephan Micus
- **Karma Collection 2003 -**
  The Ministry of Sound
- **Paint the Sky with Stars -**
  Enya
- **Time After Time -**
  Eva Cassidy
- **Behind the Sun -**
  Chicane
- **Yoga Zone: Music for Meditation -**
  Windham Hill
- **Adagio: Music for Meditation -**
  Peter Davison

RECIPES FOR RELAXATION

The Perfect Cup of Tea

1. In a teapot, place 1 tsp. of chosen tea per cup of water.
2. Boil the water, letting it cool slightly.
3. For best results, steep the tea less than 5 minutes.
4. Pour and enjoy! (Add honey for a hint of sweetness.)

A hot cup of chamomile tea is a source of comfort, nurture, and relaxation.

Design Your Own Relaxation Ritual

Relaxing is different for everyone. Make a list of everything that is relaxing to you and keep it in a special place.
As you find new things that you would like to try, add it to the list!

1. Get a piece of paper and pen.
2. Write down all the events and circumstances that may have challenged you or been stressful today.
3. Be as complete or succinct as you choose, but write them down!
4. Throw the paper away and release your attachment to the day!

Make an Herb Garden

Digging in the dirt or playing with plants can often be a relaxing meditation.

1. Purchase some good-quality potting soil and 3-5, 4" pots.
2. Choose some herbs that you enjoy.
3. Plant the herbs and watch them grow.

Some Herbs to Help You Relax

Basil: purifies the mind and opens the heart

Lemon Balm: reduces insomnia and nervous tension

Sage: eases restlessness and enhances relaxation

photo credits: